Usborne

Lots of things to spot at School

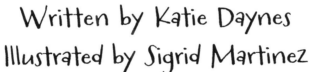

Written by Katie Daynes

Illustrated by Sigrid Martinez

Designed by Catherine-Anne MacKinnon and Helen Lee

Edited by Ruth Brocklehurst

With thanks to Rosa and Joe and everyone at Laneshaw Bridge Primary School

Each big scene in this book shows a different event in the school day or year. There are lots of things to spot and talk about on each page, and games to play.

These six animals work at the school. They appear in every scene. Can you find them all?

Lenny the lion teaches P.E.

Hetty the hippo is in charge of the school.

Percy the penguin is the school handyman.

Kai the koala teaches the older animals.

Bernie the badger teaches art.

Zara the zebra teaches the younger animals.

There's a golden trophy to spot in every scene too.

Contents

Time for school

Can you find each of these things?  slide  Piano

4

In the classroom

How many glasses of milk are on the tray?

Spot three differences between the two car paintings.

How many of these things can you find?  rockets  balls

Playtime

Can you find each of these things? watering can postman

 basketball hoop

 pair of binoculars

 chessboard

9

Lunchtime

How many of each of these things can you spot?

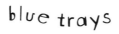 blue trays

 bananas

10

green ukuleles

yellow cups

blue striped scarfs

11

School show

big sun

spinning wheel

shield

Spring fair

How many of each of these things can you count?

 ice creams

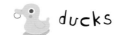 ducks

Cherry Tree School Spring Fair

Can you spot 3 differences in the clown pictures?

 coconuts

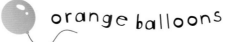 orange balloons

 bicycles

Museum trip

Egyptian Room

Do you know where the picnic area is?

Spot three differences between the two shields.

Picnic Area

AMMONITE

Dinosaurs

ROME

Diplodocus

Find a fossil

Can you spot each of these things?

triceratops skull

knight's suit

pharaoh's mask

model boat

statue of a Roman

Science day

Lots of science and fun for everyone

Our museum trip

How many dark rings can you count inside the tree trunk?

Class 5

Can you see the photo of us with the dinosaur skeleton?

Try our pinhole cameras

Can you spot each of these things?

 owl

 pink flower

Which sunflower is the tallest?

Play the pots and pans

Where is Lennie launching his rocket?

Test what's magnetic

 microscope

 exploding volcano

 spaghetti Pyramid

Sports day

How many of each of these things can you count?

 medals

 cones

End of the year

 model dinosaurs

 boxes of chocolates

 solar systems

Games

Look back through the scenes in the book to spot these things.

Can you find these pictures?

plane

leaf rubbings

snail

my dad

dinosaur

Find these musical instruments!

red ukulele

piano

trumpet

red drum

Where can you see these books?

Trees

Bella Bear

Butterflies

BUGS

Cats

Owl

Dinosaurs

Flowers

25

Use the stickers to dress us up for our own school show.

Lenny is a fireman.

Percy is a king.

Hetty is a flower.

What comes next in the alphabet? Choose the right letter stickers.

a

Count the objects and put the right number stickers in the boxes.

26

Zara is a fairy.

Kai is a knight.

Bernie is a scientist.

Find 5 differences between the 2 pictures below.

27

28

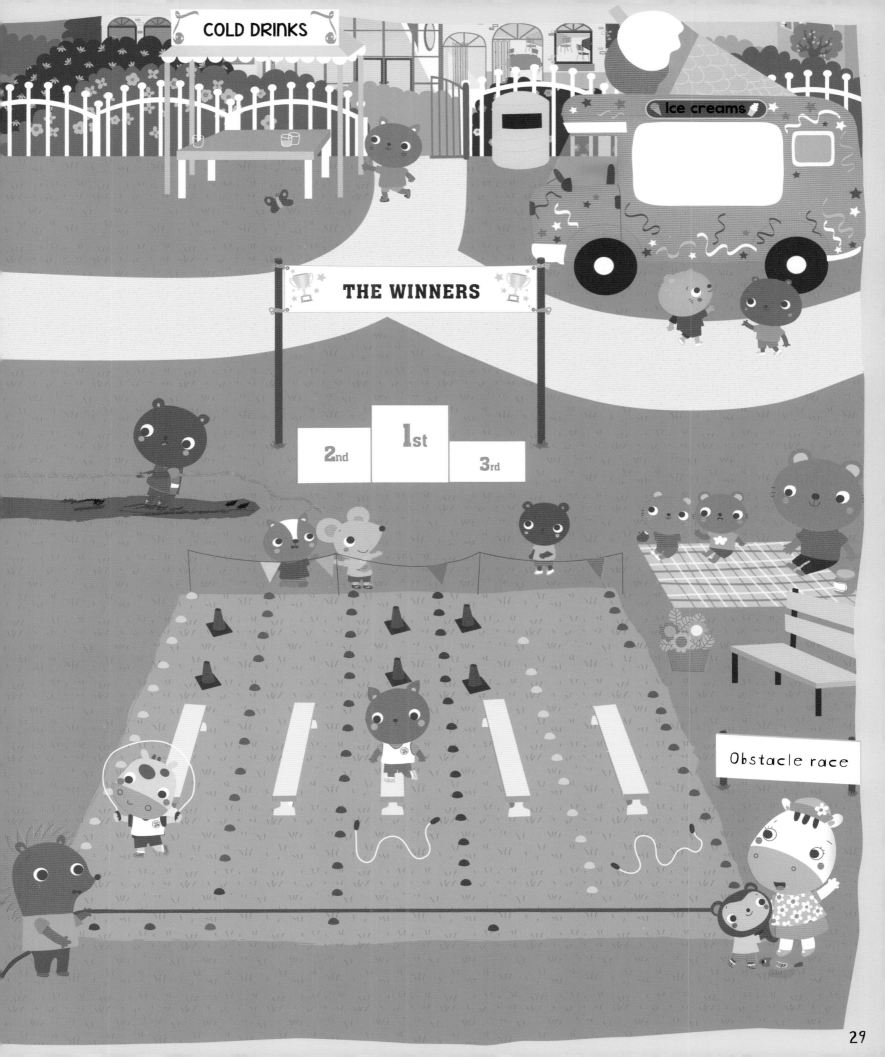

Answers

4-5 Time for school

The time is 9 o'clock.

Leave bikes here.

star on the playground

running for the bus

slide

piano

stop sign

school bell

bus stop

6-7 In the classroom

There are 2 rockets, 4 balls, 3 easels, 2 wheelbarrows and 3 yellow helmets.

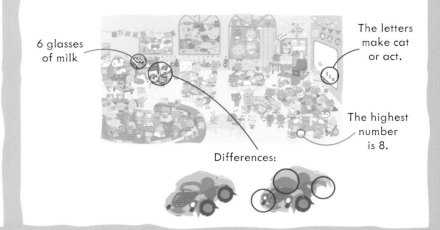

6 glasses of milk

The letters make cat or act.

The highest number is 8.

Differences:

8-9 Playtime

There are 5 dancers wearing shorts.

school kitchen

friend in red hat and scarf

blackbird

watering can

postman

basketball hoop

pair of binoculars

chessboard

10-11 Lunchtime

It's pasta, pizza, carrots, peas, cake and fruit for lunch. There are 2 snowmen. There are 5 blue trays, 4 bananas, 2 green ukuleles, 10 yellow cups and 4 blue striped scarfs.

singing group

The friend is juggling 3 red apples.

12-13 School show

There are 8 boxes of popcorn. Kai is conducting the band.

brother at front end of horse

tree walking up ramp

Dad in green hat

 crown

 crib

 big sun

 spinning wheel

 shield

14-15 Spring fair

There are 6 ice creams, 6 ducks, 5 coconuts, 5 orange balloons and 2 bicycles.

fire engine

puppet show

There are 2 big cakes left.

Grandma with blue teddy bear

Differences:

16-17 Museum trip

2 children are dressed in white togas.

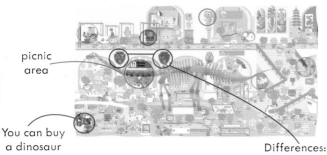

picnic area

You can buy a dinosaur T-shirt here.

Differences:

triceratops skull

knight's suit

pharaoh's mask

model boat

statue of a Roman

18-19 Science day

There are 6 dark rings inside the tree trunk. Sunflower 6 is the tallest.

photo of class with dinosaur skeleton

Lennie launching his rocket

owl

pink flower

microscope

exploding volcano

spaghetti pyramid

20-21 Sports day

2 sack racers have fallen over. There are 3 animals on each Tug of War team. There are 7 medals, 10 cones, 2 picnic blankets, 4 striped sun hats and 5 sacks.

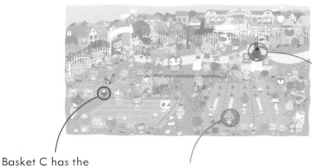

friend in black cap

Basket C has the most balls in it.

Number 3 is winning the obstacle race.

22-23 End of the year

There are 2 tree climbers. There are 4 green scooters, 6 bunches of flowers, 2 model dinosaurs, 3 boxes of chocolates and 2 solar systems.

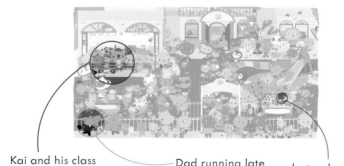

Kai and his class having photo taken

Dad running late

lost red coat

Games

PICTURES

Plane: page 6. Leaf rubbings: page 8.
Snail: page 18. My dad: page 22.
Dinosaur: page 17.

MUSICAL INSTRUMENTS

Red ukulele: page 10. Piano: page 5.
Trumpet: page 13. Red drum: page 9.

BOOKS

Trees: page 6. Bella Bear: page 15.
Butterflies: page 19. Bugs: page 23.
Cats: page 6. Owl: page 6.
Dinosaurs: page 16. Flowers: page 19.

WHICH LESSONS?
— To ballet
— To science
— To singing
— To numbers

ALPHABET

| a | b | c | d | e |

HOW MANY?

3 watering cans

8 ice creams

10 balloons

5 differences:

With thanks to Matthew Bromley, Laura Nelson, Mike Olley and Caroline Day.

Put us in the right classes on page 25.

These items will be useful in the classes too. Who needs what?

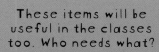

Use these stickers to dress us up on pages 26-27.

Lenny

Percy

Hetty

Zara

Kai

Bernie

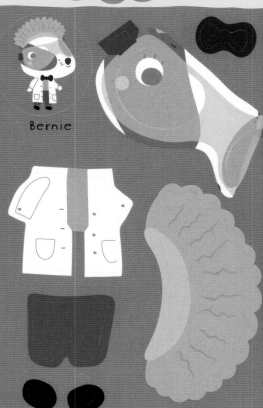